800
C

The
Sparrow
Bush

BY ELIZABETH COATSWORTH

The Sparrow Bush
Poems
Summer Green

Cricket and the Emperor's Son
The Cat Who Went to Heaven
Ronnie and the Chief's Son
Alice All-By-Herself
The Captain's Daughter
The Cat and the Captain
The Little Haymakers
Sword of the Wilderness
Away Goes Sally
The Fair American
Five Bushel Farm
The Wishing Pear
Boston Bells
Old Whirlwind
The Sod House

The
Sparrow Bush

rhymes by Elizabeth Coatsworth

wood engravings by Stefan Martin

W • W • Norton & Company • Inc • New York

To the sparrow bush at Vassar, and to Ki, Karen, and Elizabeth, who never passed it without a glance and a smile.

Contents

Preface

From the dawn of history, poetry has been man's noble companion and friend. Poetry is the voice of the heart. When the pulse quickens and the breath comes faster, the voice falls into new rhythms, and the chant begins, the ritual chant of religion, the work chant when bodies must move in unison, the chant of the harper praising the chieftain and telling the story of his exploits. Early poetry was distinguished by rhythm, not by rhyme.

During those ages when few or none could read, these epic poems contained the history of the people. They gave a meaning to courage and endurance, to loyalty and love. As book learning appeared and became general, the old poetry of the race retreated between the covers of books — or was lost — and a new poetry took its place, more personal in nature, the individual expression of individual feelings, often expressed in rhyme as well as in rhythm.

But even today, a certain racial emotion seems to underlie much poetry, and it is said that not only do poets catch the spirit of our times (when other people have not yet realized what changes are taking place) but they seem to foresee the future, and our greater poets retain something of the powers of prophecy.

But rhymes are a different matter altogether. Rhymes are made up of such things as jingles repeated to amuse children, lullabies, old saws, counting-out games, limericks, anything informal and easy-going, with a rocking-horse rhythm and a simple versification. One doesn't look for beauty in rhymes, though sometimes one may find a little. One may even find a sudden shaft of strangeness. But mostly what one will find are playfulness and good humor.

Rhyme is poetry in petticoats.

Elizabeth Coatsworth

The
Sparrow
Bush

May Morning

A joy of apple blossoms,
A flowering of cows,
The fern uncurling in the green,
The shine where water sings—
Something has found a burrow,
Each song bird has her nest,
Now! Now! The crow in the bright sun
Has white and glassy wings!

When the Wind and the Rain

When the wind and the
    rain
(Mixed with sleet) strike
    the pane,
With a rattle and
    flapping,
Like canvas sails
    snapping,
And the trees bend
    and twist,
In the wet, driving
    mist,
Oh, I'm glad as can
    be,
That I'm not on the
    sea
In this shaking and
    prowling,
This quaking and howling,
This fury and fog,
When the fields are all
    bog,
And the sky is all ocean,
And the air all commotion,—
But have just what I need:
A good book to read,
And a place, nice and warm,
Well out of the storm!

Before Breakfast

I went out in the early morning,
I went out when the house was
    asleep,
The air was cool and the wind
    hadn't risen,
And my feet got wet where
    the grass grew deep.

I felt so alone, the only one waking,
I felt so excited, I don't know
    why.
Even the birds were not yet
    flying,
Even the clouds didn't move
    in the sky.

But the robins! the robins! how
    they were singing!
Each one alone in the top of a tree,
Singing so loud (and all before
    breakfast)
Such a fine song for the
    sunrise and me!

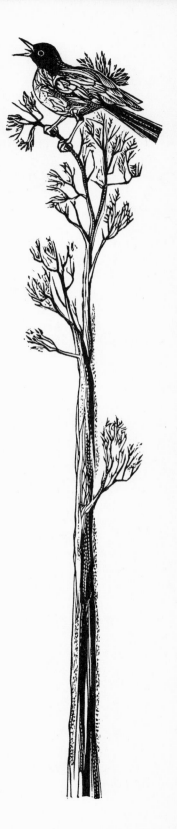

And A Big Black Crow Is Cawing

Mud in the road and wind in my hair,
Mud in the road and I don't care,
Snow in the shadows, but the fields are all
                bare,
And a big black crow is cawing.

Pussy willows close to the bough,
Catkins swinging and greening now,
Chickens feeling perky and kicking up a
                row,
And a big black crow is cawing.

Sap buckets hanging on our sugar maple tree,
Wild things stirring where no one can see,
I'm waiting for what's going to happen to
                me—
And a big black crow is cawing.

Or Hounds to Follow on a Track?

I wonder where the clouds go?
I wonder what the wind says?
I wonder what it is makes snow?
      And how the birds get back?

I wonder how the flowers grow,
So many colors from one earth?
And how it is that feathers know
      Which should be brown or red or black?

I wonder where the clouds go?
I wonder what the wind says?
Who teaches roosters how to crow?
      Or hounds to follow on a track?

The Fish

When I was very little—
It seems now like a dream—
I stood upon a little bridge
Above a little stream.

I had an alder fishing pole,
A line, and a bent pin,
And when I'd fished a little while
I pulled a sun fish in.

It was a very little fish
With rainbows on its side.
I caught it without any help
Much to my father's pride.

And yet there was a sadness, too,
That never fades away.
I don't go fishing any more:
I fished enough that day.

I Took a Little Stick

Spring tried and tried, but could not make
The water run beneath the snow,
I took a little stick and scratched
A way for it to go.

It curved into a waterfall
(I cleared the drain, so it might sing)—
Oh, I've been busy half the day
Just helping Spring.

Running Moon

Sometimes when we drive out at night
I see the half moon, thin and white.
It runs beside us like a hound,
It's there whenever I turn round.

I say, "Good moon, come on, good moon!
It won't be long, we'll be home soon,"
And when we stop, there in the sky
The moon stands still, as still as I.

The House Plants

The house plants always have
                a look
Of prisoners staring through
                the bars,
They miss the air and
                grass and stars.

And so I always talk
                with them,
And touch them with
                my softest hand,
To show them that I understand.

All the Fishes Far Below

When it rains on the sea
All the fishes far below
    Somehow know,
And like flocks of birds they wheel,
    Wheel and dart,
    Dart and wheel,
As if it were a party,
Or a holiday parade,
    Or a circus cavalcade,
For every fish's heart
Overflows with gaiety
As the sweet, fresh-water raindrops
    Fall and mingle,
    Fall and mingle
With the sea!

Asleep

I woke up early, feeling scared.
In all the house I heard no stir.
I thought, "I'll go to Mother's room
And creep into the bed with her."

But at the door I stopped to look.
She did not speak nor turn to smile.
I dared not move, but stared and
                stared,
And she grew stranger all the while.

It seemed to me some enemy
Was lying in my mother's place,
With eyes closed tight to shut
                me out,
         And a forgetting face.

Like Arrows

When I walk, I very often look down.
A road has so many things that I
        like to see:
The shapes and colors of pebbles, speckled or
        brown,
The marks of tires when it's rained
        recently,
Perhaps my own footprints from another
        day,
Or a feather or curious stick, but
        most of all
Deer tracks, like arrows pointed all one
        way,
Gentle and beautiful arrows that
        never fall.

Deer at Dusk

I stood so still
It wasn't I who scared them.
I was in the house, so it couldn't have been I,
But suddenly the three deer went
      leaping across the pasture,
Their white tails flashing and
      their heads held high,
Over the wall and into the woods they
      went soaring,
Running as swallows fly.

The Lilac Spires

The lilac spires are rusty,
The butterflies in doubt
Hover among their towers
Scenting last sweetness out,
Bewildered and uncertain
Fluttering about.

The lilac spires are rusty,
So short their lovely hour,
No longer in their balconies
The bee sings to the flower,
The music now is silent
That thrummed from bower to bower.

Tracks in the Snow

Wherever fox or cat or crow
Has walked in this new-fallen snow
He leaves a chain of prints. I see
Them make a path from him to me.
Some of them loop and some go straight.
If I could follow by wall and gate,
By wood and field, sometime, I know,
I'd find that fox or cat or crow,
And many others: squirrel, mouse,
The big dog from next-door house,
The weasel and the fleeing hare,
The deer, oh, all of them are there
At their end of the track, while I
Stand at my end and stare and sigh.
But there was a big track one day;
I think a bear had gone that way.
Then I was very glad that he
Was at the other end from me!

Candy House

The icicles beneath our eaves
Hang down like candy canes,
Rock-candy canes as clear as glass,
And I can hear them when I pass
Playing small tunes with icy beads
That drip on what was grass.

They melt in sun and bend in wind,
And cling to window panes.
The roof is frosted deep with snow
And with the icicles in a row
Our house looks like a candy house
In tales of long ago.

Hansel and Gretel might come here,
Tiptoeing near to taste.
They would be safe the livelong day,
No witch would ever rush their way,
But only I'd run to the door
And ask them in to play.

The Two Cats

I'm very good friends with both our cats,
I've known them since they were kittens.
And one is little and one has big paws,
And their names are Midget and Mittens.

But sometimes at dusk when we're driving home
And come on the cats by surprise,
I feel a shiver go down my back
Facing their burning eyes.

Storm at Night

When I'm tucked into bed,
Comfortable and warm,
I often think of animals
    Outside in the storm:

The deer in hemlock thickets,
(A little out of the rain),
A wet fox going on his rounds
    For supper once again;

Hungry hares in their burrows;
A flood in the woodchuck's hole;
Chipmunks cuddled together;
    A half-drowned, star-nosed mole.

I lie in my bed and shiver
And think of what Father said,
"If you were a creature of the woods,
You wouldn't like house and bed!"

The Chair House

When it's raining,
    And raining,
        And raining,
With a drip and a drizzle and a drop,
The porch is so cool and so pleasant,
The rain falls, hippity hop,
And I take a porch chair and
        upturn it,
With a blanket to serve as a door,
And I put in a pillow or pillows
To make a soft place on the floor.

There it is, dark and safe: it's an igloo,
Or perhaps it's an African hut.
I crawl in and the door drops
        behind me,
It's a wonderful house, but . . . but . . . ,
It's so small, there's no place to go to,
It's so dark, there is nothing to do,
So soon I lift up the blanket,
And, looking about me, crawl through.

Yet though I don't stay, I still love it,
I dream of my chair house at night,
And I hear the rain calling
And falling,
As I curl myself up, out of sight.

Ice Storm

As I was walking down our lane,
My head held low, my head held low,
I hardly looked above my feet
The cold north wind was blowing so.

I heard a little rustling sound
Complaining that I would not see,
Until at last I looked, and there,
Beside me, stood a young birch tree.

The little tree seemed made of glass,
All bright and glittering in the sun,
And from a bough, a leaf hung down
The only one, the only one.

And still the little leaf complained,
Until at last I raised my eyes
High to the treetops all ablaze
With a cold fire against the skies.

And as I looked and looked and looked
Forgetting that the wind was cold,
The withered leaf hung still once more,
Its message heard, its story told.

Rhyme

I like to see a thunder storm,
A dunder storm,
A blunder storm,
I like to see it, black and slow,
Come stumbling down the hills.

I like to hear a thunder storm,
A plunder storm,
A wonder storm,
Roar loudly at our little house
And shake the window sills!

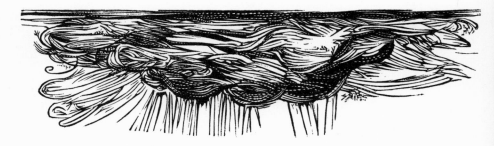

To a Day Moon

Aren't you cold up there in the windy sky?
Don't you feel how the north wind stings?
My cheeks are red, but you're white as a cloud,
And seem thinking of other things.
You don't seem to think of the arctic wind,
You don't seem to think of the cold,
But maybe of wonderful things you saw
Before the world grew old.

All on a Christmas Morning

I saw a robin
        and four of his friends,
All on a Christmas
        morning.
He came to the road
        where the woodland
                ends,
And with him were four of his high-
        stepping friends,
All on a Christmas
        morning.

His head was cocked
        and his breast was
                red,
All on a Christmas morning.
I hope he has a warm
        place for a bed
And can ask his friends home
        to a barn or a shed,
All on a Christmas morning.

I hope he has
        berries and seeds
                to eat,
All on a Christmas
        morning.
Good luck to you,
        robin! And
        many a treat
For you and your friends!
        Oh! plenty to eat!
On a cold, bright Christmas
        morning!

Three

We were just three,
Two loons and me.
They swam and fished,
I watched and wished,
That I, like them, might dive and play
In icy waters all the day.
I watched and wished. I could not reach
Where they were, till I tried their speech,
And something in me helped, so I
Could give their trembling sort of cry.
One loon looked up and answered me.
He understood that we were three.

Early Dark

Night's all right
With stars and a moon,
But night's all wrong
In the afternoon!
It drops from the trees
And it creeps on the floor,
And they call me in
By half past four!

The Two Mirrors

The mirror in my mother's room
Is big and old and dim and kind.
"How very nice you look today,"
My mother's mirror likes to say,
"Yes, really, very nice!"

The little mirror in my room
Asks in a horrid voice,
"Slept in your clothes again, my dear?"
"You've lost your comb and brush, I fear!"
And then—it gives advice.

Heigh-ho!

Heigh-ho!
    How the weeks go!
      It was May
        It was June
          And now it's July!

Every fledgling has learned to fly,
And how quickly, how softly, the rose
    petals fall!
Green peas fill the pod, and the
    dragonfly
Is moored to the water-lily leaf,
And hollyhocks heighten along the
    wall.
The days are long, but the season is brief.
Shorn of their grasses, the hay fields lie.

It was May
    It was June
      And now it's July!

Some Day

Whenever I go down to the shore
There's something I am looking for.
I don't think it can be the pond;
It's not the low green hills beyond;
It's not raccoon tracks in the sand
Like prints of a thin baby's hand;
It's not a muskrat swimming by;
It's not the small clouds in the sky;
Not even the line of alewives, straight
As soldiers passing through a gate
Until a big fish comes, and then
They spatter, and go on again.
Sometimes I think the ducks might be
The thing I'm waiting there to see,
But it's not ducks.

Yet more and more,
I'm sure that some day by the shore
I'll see what I am waiting for.

Night in Early Spring

Why does the little dog stand by the door
And look towards the woods and bark and bark?
Something is stirring there in the dark,
Something that slept the winter through
And now is stirring once more.

I can stand and stand by the open door
And listen and look and wrinkle my nose,
But still I can never find out what goes
Restless under the wood-lot trees,
After the winter, restless once more.

Seen By Moonlight

I looked from my window and there
        in the moonlight,
Small and busy against the moon,
Stood old Bill Beetle. And what
        was he doing?
Spitting tobacco (oh, yes! he was
        chewing!)
And chopping away with his axe,
        sharp and bright,
Chopping away at the sweet
        honeysuckle
And buzzing a tuneless tune
        to the night.

The Lights

"Where are you off to, two by two,
Lights that hurry so fast through the
                    night?
Are your journeys short, are
                    your journeys long,
Glowing,
And flowing,
A river of light,
Two by two, through the darkness of
                    night?"
I ask the lights and they
                    don't reply,
Hurrying on through the darkness of
                    night;
They come like stars, that rush and pass,
Glowing,
And flowing,
In meteor flight,
Unwinking eyes that glare
                    through the night.

The Maple

In our big maple tree
There's a platform Father made,
And little seats high in the boughs
Where, in the deepest shade,
Inside the great, green thimble
My friends can climb with
        me
To sit a while and whisper
Within the whispering tree.

In the Blueberry Bushes

Up on our hill in the blueberry bushes
There's a wonderful horse that's made
> of stone.
I go up there when I'm all alone.
Maybe he once belonged to a wizard,
Who rode him a lot and when he grew
> old
Changed him to stone, lichened and
> cold,
Half buried in earth and the blue-
> berry bushes.
But he has a head that he holds
> up high
And a hollow saddle, and that's
> where I
Sit when I ride him across
> the world.
Sometimes we go to Italy
Or gallop dry-shod across the sea,
To sleep on green islands, or go to Peru.
No mountain's too high, no valley's too
> low
For me and my wonderful horse to
> go,

But whenever we wish, in a moment or so,
We're back in our forest of
> blueberry bushes.

When Snow Will Come

The swallows and the butterflies
Left early, so they say.
How can a monarch butterfly
Or swallow know in hot July
When snow will come? I never know
Until the snowflakes fly.
The swallows and the butterflies
Are cleverer than I!

Will This Wind Bring You?

Wild geese, wild geese! When will you fly over?
Will this wind bring you, will you bring the
           spring?
I should rather hear you, shouting in confusion,
Than listen to the song that any bird can sing.

Once in the dark I woke and heard you passing,
You sounded like a pack of beagles in full cry.
Wild geese, wild geese! When will you be
           coming?
I listen day and night to hear you going by.

Soon you will be feeding among the greening
           pastures.
We shall see you now any fine day,
Riding the river in a painted squadron
Like a fleet of galleons, far out in the
           bay.

Ducks at Twilight

Slowly, sedately, Indian file
The ducks return as the sun goes down
Back to the barnyard they know so
        well,
And the farmer's wife, smiling and brown,
Who will shut them up in their safe
        little house
Where they may slumber the long night
        through
And never fear the tiptoe fox
Nor wake for the owl's to-whit, to-whoo.

Shoe the Horse

Shoe the horse
And shoe the mare:
    (And you shall hear them
    Wherever they go).

But let the little
Colt run bare:
    (And he will be silent
    As wind over snow).

The Horses

Red horse,
Roan horse,
Black horse,
And white,
Feeding all together in the green
    summer light,

White horse,
Black horse,
Spotted horse,
And gray,
I wish that I were off with you,
    far, far away!

All of a Sudden

Galloping galloping galloping galloping,
The horses gallop along the meadows,
Click on the rocks and soft on
          the grasses,
Racing the clouds and the clouds'
          long shadows.

They run as the wind runs, they
          run like the shadows;
From their hoofs the dust drifts
          away in a haze.
Galloping galloping galloping galloping—
All of a sudden, they stop to graze!

Danger

Up and at them
Brave Fitzroy!
And Douglas, mount again!
There's thunder in the Iron Hills,
And smoke upon the main.
An eagle cried out of a cloud,
Stags fought beneath an oak,
And children, coming home from school,
Met with a rock, which spoke!

Far Away

Once a little boy
    Lived with a bear,
Went to sleep
    Against deep, brown hair,
Warm and safe
    In a hidden lair,

Gathered berries
    Where wild fruits grow,
Drank from cold streams
    Born of the snow,
Stared down at valleys
    Far below.

Though he at last
    Returned to men,
And never walked
    With the bears again,
All his life long
    He dreamed of the den.

The Starry Nevers

There is a lion which has never roared,
There is a bull whose horns have never
gored,

There are two hounds and they have
never bayed,
There is an archer, never yet afraid,

And there's an eagle which has
never soared.

There is a ram which never led a flock,
There is a maiden still bound to a rock,

There is a centaur whose hoofs make
no sound,
Two fish which swim where never sea is
found,

And a great whale which meets
no tempest's shock.

There is a swan whose wings are always
wide,
And there are twins, forever side
by side,

There is a scorpion which has never stung,
There is a bear which cannot join its
                young,

And there's a goat with shaggy
                silver hide.

There is a chair on which no one
                may sit,
There is a way, but no one travels it,

There is a dolphin leaping without spray,
There is a hare which never runs away,

And a winged horse which knows no
                spur nor bit.

There is a crab was never in the
                sea,
There is a dove which never saw a tree,

There is a raven which has never croaked,
There is a hunter, sandal-shod and cloaked,

And these all move, but oh! how
                silently!

The Frogs' Wedding

Happy is the bride in the green,
   green pond,
And happy is the groom as he
   swims beside his bride.
She carries a bouquet
In the prettiest sort of way,
And he smiles and stares about him
In his pride pride pride.

The fishes, oh, the fishes,
They all bring their kindest wishes,
And the little minnows flicker
And they snicker as they come.
But sad and alone,
Squatted down upon a stone
Sits the disappointed lover,
Looking glum glum glum.

Sudden Storm

The rain comes in sheets
Sweeping the streets,
Here, here, and here,
Umbrellas appear,
Red, blue, yellow, green,
They tilt and they lean
Like mushrooms, like flowers
That grow when it showers.

Pioneer Rat

The big rat said to the little rats,
"I'm old and my whiskers are hoar.
   I've sailed enough
   And the life is tough,
And now I'm going ashore."

The big rat said to the little rats,
"This country, from all I can hear,
   Never's known a rat,
   But I'll remedy that
And I'll be the pioneer."

The big rat said to the listening rats,
"You can stay, or come with me.
   As soon as it's dark
   I'm quitting this barque,
For I've had my fill of the sea!
I have!
I've had my fill of the sea!"

Riddle

What is it cries without a mouth?
What buffets, and yet has no hand?
And, footless, runs upon the waves
To drive them roaring up the sand?

Old as the world, unseen as Time,
Without beginning, without end,
What is it cries and has no mouth,
Wave-wrestler, and the sea-
        gulls' friend?

Crow in Springtime

The farmer plants seed
For the crow to gather.
Caw! Caw! Plant it again!

He comes with the dawn,
An insolent fellow,
Who knows all the ways and
        the habits of men!

Corn, wheat,
Barley or peas,
The crow likes them all, so plant
        them once more!

He comes like a brigand,
He comes like a thief,
And he'll leave the field bare,
        as he's left it before!

Late October

The cows are dressed in suede,
And the wild geese go by
Fleeing the cold; not so
The tender butterfly

Which o'er the dying grass
And leaves and broken ferns,
In frivolous delight
Dances and turns.

Sing a Song of Kittens

Sing a song of kittens,
Kittens full of play,
Chasing shadows, chasing tails,
Romping half the day,
Springing upon — nothing!
Scampering off — nowhere!
Glaring out of milk-blue eyes,
Lashing tails in air.

Sing a song of kittens,
Kittens tired of play,
Kittens growing sleepy
At the close of day,
Very glad to cuddle,
Very pleased to purr,
Curling up in little balls
Of thistledown and fur.

Fly Away

John, John, and his sister, Susan,
Saw a red ladybug down in the grass.

"Fly away, right away, fly away quickly!
Here's where the cows and the greedy
          hens pass.

"Fly away, fly away, back to the heavens,
Fly away, fly away, home to the sky,

"To the winds and the clouds and
          the stars of the evening,
Shining so bright and so small and so
          high!"

When Grandmama Was Young

Once upon a time
When grandmama was young,
Foxes played on bagpipes,
Raccoons beat on drums,
Mice danced minuets,
Squirrels two-stepped gaily,
And the unmarried cottontails
Gave tea parties daily.

The Sparrow Bush

I looked out at the lilac
    bush,
And all the twigs were
    sad and bare,
But while I looked, a
    flock of birds
All suddenly alighted
    there.

They were not special
    birds at all,
Just sparrows, gray, and
    black, and brown,
And some sat,
    feathers way puffed out,
And some were hopping up
    and down.

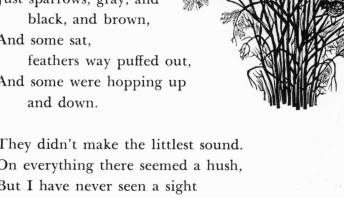

They didn't make the littlest sound.
On everything there seemed a hush,
But I have never seen a sight
As pretty as that sparrow bush.

Among the Leaves

1. The sun says nothing.
   Silent, it rejoices.
   The rain speaks in a hundred
   　　　　　changing voices.

2. Gone are the cattle,
   Yet upon the hill
   Their skein of pathways vein the
   　　　　　greenness still.

3. Old palms resemble ostriches or giraffes.
   "How beautiful," one says,
   And then—
   One laughs.

4. The hawk, far off,
   Circling the cloudless sky
   Is much diminished by this nearby fly.

5. The birds leap downward from the tops
                    of trees
Like swimmers diving into summer seas.

6. The blossoms take the lower boughs,
                    The sparrows choose the upper.
The blossoms ask for nothing.
                    The sparrows want their supper.

7. The small birds cheep and cheep.
They can't remember
The songs they left off singing in
                    September.

ABOUT THE AUTHOR

Elizabeth Coatsworth was born in Buffalo, New York. She studied for two years at the Buffalo Seminary and then attended Vassar and Columbia, where she took an M.A. degree. She spent the following year in the Orient and later enjoyed long winters in Europe, North Africa, Mexico, and Guatemala. *The Cat Who Went to Heaven,* winner of the Newbery Medal, and *The Cricket and the Emperor's Son* grew out of her memories of Japan. Many of Miss Coatsworth's other books reflect her love of New England, where she and her husband, Henry Beston, brought up their children and still live for most of the year.

Miss Coatsworth has written more than fifty books for young people as well as half-a-dozen novels and an equal number of books of poetry. Poetry to this day remains her favorite form of writing.

ABOUT THE ARTIST

Stefan Martin was born in Elgin, Illinois. He attended public schools in Hightstown and Roosevelt, New Jersey, and is a graduate of the Art Institute of Chicago. While he was earning his degree in painting Mr. Martin worked as an apprentice at an engraving company in Chicago. It was here that he learned the techniques of this precise and demanding art. It takes an hour to chisel one square inch of an engraving, and mistakes can not be erased. The engravings for this book were done on hardwood — the end grain was used — with metal engraving tools. His woodcuts are done on plank wood, soft-wood, and gouges are used. Mr. Martin teaches wood engraving and woodcutting at the Summit Art Center in Summit, New Jersey. He has twice received the Tiffany Grant in print making, and his work is included in many private collections. His children's book illustration has been honored by the A.I.G.A. in its Fifty Books of the Year Show, 1962. Mr. Martin lives with his wife and four children in Roosevelt, New Jersey.